How to use this book

Follow the advice, in italics, given for you on each page.
Praise *the children at every step!*

Detailed guidance is provided in the Read Write Inc. Phonics Handbook.

7 reading activities

Children:

☆ *Practise reading the speed sounds.*

☆ *Read the green and red words for the Ditty.*

☆ *Listen as you read the introduction.*

☆ *Read the Ditty.*

☆ *Re-read the Ditty and discuss the 'questions to talk about'.*

☆ *Re-read the Ditty with fluency and expression.*

☆ *Practise reading the speed words.*

Speed Sounds

Consonants

Say the pure sounds (do not add 'uh').

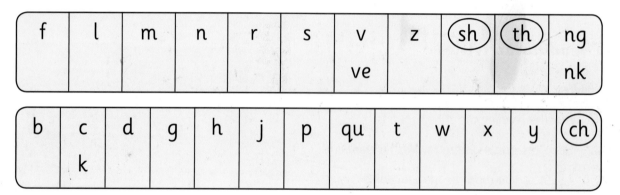

f	l	m	n	r	s	v	z	(sh)	(th)	ng
						ve				nk

b	c	d	g	h	j	p	qu	t	w	x	y	(ch)
	k											

Vowels

Say the sounds in and out of order.

a	e	i	o	u

Each box contains only one sound. Focus sounds are circled.

Ditty 1 Jam

Green words

Read in Fred Talk (pure sounds).

leg pot jam got a
plop <u>ch</u>in di<u>sh</u> and

Read the root word first and then with the ending.

lot → lots

Red words

I of my

Ditty 1 Jam

Introduction

This is a story about a girl who likes playing with her food!

I got a di<u>sh</u> and a pot of jam

plop
jam on my leg

plop
jam on my <u>ch</u>in

lots of jam

Ditty 2 # Hug hug

Green words

Read in Fred Talk (pure sounds).

leg   ted   hug   <u>th</u>is   <u>ch</u>in

tum   is

Red words

my

Ditty 2 Hug hug

Introduction

In this story we meet a boy and find out more about him.

<u>th</u>is is my leg

this is my tum

this is my chin

<u>th</u>is is my ted

Ditty 3 In the net

Green words

Read in Fred Talk (pure sounds).

got net big can yes

fat a in ha<u>ve</u> fi<u>sh</u>

Red words

I <u>the</u>

In the net

Introduction
Do you like fishing? The girl in this story likes fishing, but she keeps catching the wrong things!

I ha<u>ve</u> got a big net

a log in <u>the</u> net

a can in <u>the</u> net

yes

a fat fi<u>sh</u> in <u>the</u> net

Questions to talk about

Ditty 1

What two things does the girl get at the start of the story?

Where does the jam go first?

Have you ever been told off for being a messy eater?

Ditty 2

What is the first thing the boy points to?

Do you think the boy likes his teddy?

What is your favourite cuddly toy?

Ditty 3

What is the second thing the girl catches?

Why is the girl happy at the end of the story?

What sort of things do you like doing at home?

Speed words for Ditty 1

Children practise reading the words across the rows, down the columns and in and out of order clearly and quickly.

leg	jam	chin	pot	a
of	plop	I	dish	got

Speed words for Ditty 2

leg	this	chin	my
tum	is	this	hug

Speed words for Ditty 3

a	got	the	big	fat
net	fish	can	yes	in